CHANGES
in the NIGHT

by Heather Eyles

Illustrated by Tim Beer

LONGMAN

INTRODUCTION

While I was writing this play I had some ideas about how you might actually put on *Changes in the Night* as a show in school, or at the end of term, or for Christmas.

I think it's very helpful to have some idea of what it would look like, even if you are just going to read the play in class, so that you can picture it in your mind's eye and imagine all your friends taking part. You may have much better ideas than mine, in which case you could have a discussion about the best ways to put it on, and especially how to do the difficult bits.

'Difficult bits' are always a problem for the director of a play (a director is the person who decides what the show looks like and arranges rehearsals for the actors) and can give you a headache. The really difficult bit in this play comes with the tiger scene because I think it would look silly to have someone dressed up in a tiger suit leaping about on stage. No one would believe it was a real tiger and everyone might laugh!

I think what would be really good would be a large cardboard cut-out of a tiger, like a huge shadow puppet which would be carried through the air by one or two children; in a way a 'representation' of a tiger. This could be used for other things in the doll's house too, such as a big cut-out ship, and a jack-in-the-box, a toy soldier and a teddy. All kinds of things could come and go on the stage in this way, carried by children, and then they could be taken away when the scene is over and the modern day comes back.

That's my thought about the 'difficult bit'– you may have a better idea.

So – in general I always think that it's best to keep it simple so there are fewer distractions for your audience. Obviously you have to have a doll's house on stage. When anything is changed in the doll's house then the huge cardboard figures could appear and move, so everybody can *see* what is happening larger than life.

The modern day set can be very simple – you don't need much furniture – and the transformation can be done with the cardboard figures.

What would be a great help in producing an atmosphere would be a group of musicians at the side of the stage playing some appropriate music on recorders and percussion, such as xylophones.

For the Christmas scenes you could have some well-known Christmas tunes and then all sorts of spooky percussion music for things that happen in the house, like on films. If that's too difficult or would take too long to rehearse, you can leave it out in performance, but it's nice to imagine it when you are reading the parts.

So, have a good time reading the play together, and if you can imagine it in your school hall with all the school watching and all the exciting things going on, then I think you'll enjoy it all the more.

CHANGES *in the* NIGHT

CHARACTERS

Roger
A boy, aged about ten

Elizabeth
His sister, aged about six

Mum

Dad

Sarah
A Victorian child, about seven years old

Nanny
Her Victorian nanny

Cook

Scene setter

SCENE 1

Scene setter   It's Christmas Day and Roger and Elizabeth are running around squealing and chasing each other.

Mum   Roger! Elizabeth! Stop it! It'll end in tears!

Roger   She started it!

Elizabeth   He started it!

Roger	Liar!
Elizabeth	Liar yourself.
Mum	Stop it, stop it you two. Can't we ever have any peace from you two squabbling – even on Christmas Day?
Roger	She's jealous, she wants my watch. My lovely waterproof, digital watch, with stopwatch, six time zones and compass.
Elizabeth	Don't!
Roger	Do!
Elizabeth	Don't!
Mum	Stop it, stop it you two. You'll drive me mad. It'll be lunch in a minute – if we last that long. Elizabeth, run and fetch your dad, you've got one more present each to open before lunch.
Elizabeth	Dad!
Dad	Hallo?
Mum	We're going to open *the present.*
Dad	Oh, right. I'd better be present then. Ho! ho!
Scene setter	Dad often makes jokes that no one laughs at.
Mum	Here you are, Roger.
Roger	Thanks, Mum. Oh, great – a new computer game! "Sonic Worm." Can I go and play it?

Dad	No, not just yet. Elizabeth has got to open hers yet. It's over here.
Elizabeth	Is that mine? It's very big.
Dad	Open it then.
Elizabeth	Oh ... It's a doll's house. Pooh!
Mum	It's a very special doll's house. It belonged to your great granny. Your dad's done it up for you. Are you listening? I want you to be very careful with it.
Scene setter	But Elizabeth isn't listening, she's pinching Roger.
Mum	Are you listening?!
Elizabeth	Uh huh. When's lunch?
Dad	Oh really, Elizabeth. I thought you might take a bit of interest. It's lovely, look.
Roger	Can I see inside?
Elizabeth	No. It's mine.
Roger	I only want to have a look.
Dad	Of course you can, Roger. You've got to learn to share, Elizabeth.
Roger	Oh! It's the most beautiful thing I've ever seen in my whole life! Masses of food made out of plaster, looking good enough to eat!
Mum	Jellies and jams, pink blancmange, a giant

ham, a golden chicken, a scaly fish with pop-eyes, some tiny, shiny brown eggs in a basket, a crusty cottage loaf, a Christmas cake with a tiny snowman on top, a pork pie.

Roger   My favourite food!

Dad   Strings of onions, tins of biscuits.

Roger   Oh, such biscuits, with pink and white icing on them. And best of all a tray of glossy, dark-brown chocolates, with squiggles and cherries on the top.

Dad	Don't forget the cook – to cook it all.
Roger	Look at the nursery – all those toys.
Elizabeth	No, don't touch – it's mine.
Dad	Now, Elizabeth, that's selfish.
Elizabeth	Well it is mine, isn't it? You gave it to me.
Dad	Well yes, but ...
Elizabeth	Then he can't touch it.
Roger	It's all right, I don't want to touch her silly old house anyway. It's stupid.

Elizabeth	You're stupid.
Roger	Oh shut up!
Mum	Now you two, you'll be sent to your rooms if you go on like this – it's Christmas Day – remember?
Roger	Sorry Mum, but she's driving me nuts.
Mum	I know. Maybe she'll feel differently after lunch and you can play with it then.
Elizabeth	Won't. He's never going to play with it. Never. I want to go to the park and fly my new kite.

SCENE 2

Scene setter   It's night time and Elizabeth gets into her bed and goes to sleep. Then Roger comes into the room.

Roger   It's not fair. They only gave it to her because she's a girl. It's not fair, it's not fair. I like it more than she does. It's wasted on *her*.

Scene setter   Roger creeps over to the doll's house to have a closer look.

Roger   Toy soldiers all in a row, a rocking horse with a real mane. A teddy, a doll and a clown, and a jack-in-the-box sitting on a chest of drawers, and two beds – a boy and girl doll. I'll show her. Meany. Horrible meany. I'll show her for not letting me play with it. I'll take that ... and that ... and that.

Scene setter   Roger takes some food from the doll's house kitchen and puts the things into his pyjama pocket. He slips into bed, looking longingly over to the doll's house. He goes to sleep.

SCENE 3

Scene setter   Later, Roger wakes up and looks around. He rubs his eyes. He shakes his head and tries to go back to sleep again, because he thinks he's dreaming. His bedroom has mysteriously changed into the nursery of the doll's house. After a few seconds he sits bolt upright. He fingers the Victorian nightshirt he is now wearing. Gingerly he gets out of bed. He looks carefully at a strange girl in the bed opposite him from all angles. He walks round all the objects in the room, touching them.

Roger   I'm dreaming. I know I'm dreaming. But I'm wide awake. What's happening to me? And who is that in the bed? Shall I wake her up? Ask her what's going on? Better not. She might get a surprise if she finds me here. I wonder what her name is. Mmm ... this book must be hers. "*Sarah's book*" – well that's solved that mystery. I think I'd better go back to bed – then I can wake up and find it was all just a dream. Just a minute though! I'm hungry! And all that lovely food just waiting for me down in the kitchen. I feel like a midnight snack.

Scene setter   Roger goes downstairs to the kitchen. His mouth is watering at the thought of all that food. As he opens the kitchen door, Cook appears! She grabs Roger and shakes him.

Cook   What do you think you're doing, you little whippersnapper? Stealing again, I'll be bound. I'll give you stealing! That's for my pork pie! And that's for my chocolates! And that's for my lovely iced biscuits that were for Miss Sarah's birthday! Eh! What do you say to that? There, and if you go running off and telling Madam or that Nanny that I laid so much as a finger on you, I'll have your guts for garters. Do you hear me?

Scene setter   She picks Roger up and throws him out of the door. Roger shakes all over and tries not to cry. Then he creeps back up the stairs to the nursery, and crouches by the fire, warming his hands. He starts to cry. Sarah sits up in bed and looks at him.

Sarah   Why are you crying, Roger? Have you got into trouble again? Did Cook catch you? I bet she gave you a shaking.

Roger   Y- y- y- yes. I took some food and hid it in my pocket and ...

Sarah   Have you still got it?

Roger   Yes, no .... I mean ...

Sarah   Never mind. Have a crumpet.

Roger   (speaking to himself) She talks to me as if she knows me very well. How can that be

when she's never met me before? But I do know her name. Um ... Sarah?

Sarah	Yes?
Roger	Oh ... It must be nearly time to get up.
Sarah	Oh yes. Another beastly day with beastly Nanny. Why does she always have to be so strict and stiff? If I were a nanny I'd be nice to my charges and buy them ices in the park and let them climb trees and oh – oh everything. Let's run away! I'm so unhappy I can't bear it a moment longer. We could go to – to –
Roger	Brighton?
Sarah	Yes, Brighton. And we could go on the pier and we could eat ices until we were sick. That would show them. Nobody cares tuppence about us.
Roger	Don't they?
Sarah	You know they don't. Papa's always at the club and Mamma's always out at her meetings. I don't think they'd even notice if we were gone. Only Nanny would because she wouldn't have anyone to be beastly to any more.
Roger	Absolutely.
Sarah	Shall we then?

Roger	Shall we what?
Sarah	Run away. Sssh ... someone's coming!
Scene setter	Sarah and Roger hear the heavy sound of footsteps coming towards the door. They look at each other in fear.
Sarah	Oh my goodness – Nanny! Quick! Into bed!
Scene setter	Nanny opens the door.
Nanny	Master Roger, Miss Sarah – How dare you get out of your beds at this hour of the morning? As a punishment there will be no walk in the

park today. Let that be understood!

Scene setter Nanny leaves.

Roger Phew! Thank goodness she's gone.

Sarah Better go back to sleep.

Roger Mmmm. I think we'd better.

SCENE 4

Scene setter It's morning and Roger is still asleep.

Elizabeth Wake up! Wake up! We're going to the pantomime today! We're going to the pantomime. Hurry up, I'm going to get washed.

Scene setter Roger slowly sits up and looks around. Then he creeps out of bed and goes over to the doll's house. He stares at it and gingerly reaches out his hand to take a doll.

Roger Nanny! So that's who you are. And very disagreeable you look too! What a grumpy-looking doll!

Elizabeth Come on, Roger – Mum says you've got to hurry up or we'll miss the train.

Roger OK, OK, I'm coming.

Scene setter Roger puts the Nanny and the food back into the doll's house.

SCENE 5

Scene setter   That evening, when he is ready for bed, Roger opens the doll's house once again, but Elizabeth comes in – in time to catch him.

Elizabeth   Leave it alone!

Roger   But I ...

Elizabeth   It's mine. You mustn't touch it.

Roger   Oh shut up!

Elizabeth   Mum!

Roger   I'm not touching it! I hate you.

Elizabeth   I hate you too – stupid brain! They're my dolls and I'm going to play with Lucy.

Roger   She's not called Lucy. Her name's Sarah!

Elizabeth   How do you know?

Roger   It's on the front of her book, look!

Elizabeth   I don't care about the stupid book. She's Lucy. Lucy – Lucy – stupid brain!

Roger   I'll get you!

Elizabeth   Oh no you won't! I'm going to bed.

Roger   (speaking to himself) Horrible, horrible, horrible. I'll show her!

Scene setter   Roger takes Nanny's hat from the doll's house and puts it in the flour bin in the kitchen. Then Roger marches off to bed and gets in. He lies down, then sits up as if he is thinking – looking worried. Eventually he goes to sleep.

Scene setter When Roger wakes up he looks around. He knows he is back in the doll's house. Nanny marches in and Roger disappears under the covers. Nanny walks over to his bed and pulls the covers off him. Then she does the same to Sarah.

Nanny Master Roger, Miss Sarah – when one is in charge of two children such as you, one learns to expect lapses in decorum, even an excess of high spirits, but I have learned to expect much, much worse. WILFUL DISOBEDIENCE, WICKEDNESS AND DEPRAVITY! Do you understand me?

Sarah No, Nanny.

Nanny Impudence! I will ask you one time and one time only, and I expect a truthful answer. Where is my best hat?

Scene setter A terrible shriek echoes through the house.

Nanny Heaven preserve us! That's Cook! Whatever is the matter?

Cook Oh me Lawd! Oh me Lawd! Give me the fright of me life it did. Look what I just found in the flour bin, all among my best white cake flour. Thought it was a rat I did. Give me such a turn!

Nanny	Give it to me, Cook. It is my hat I believe. Thank you. That will be all.
Cook	Yes, Nanny.
Roger	It was me! It was me! It wasn't Sarah at all. She didn't know anything about it. I did it all by myself!
Nanny	I shall not enquire as to why you felt it necessary to perpetrate this evil. I shall just confine you to the attic wardrobe for the rest of the day, as is the punishment fitting for such a crime.
Sarah	Oh no, Nanny! Not the attic wardrobe. Please, Nanny! You know how much he hates it!
Nanny	I will have no impertinence. It is a fitting and just punishment. Make yourself ready, boy. And Cook, bread and water only today for this – for this – hooligan!
Cook	Yes, Nanny. (*speaking to herself*) Oh but I do feel sorry for the poor little dears.

Scene setter Nanny takes Roger by the ear and leads him up the stairs to the wardrobe. Then she shuts the door on him and leaves him there. Roger sits in the cold – he shivers and hugs himself as the time crawls by. He only has spiders for company.

Scene 7

Sarah Psst – Roger.

Roger Sarah?

Sarah I've got some chocolates for you. Cook gave them to me. She said she couldn't bear the thought of you being locked in a wardrobe all day with nothing nice to eat. She's a good soul really.

Roger Push them under the door – oh thanks! You're very brave. Don't get caught.

Sarah I won't. Nanny's having her afternoon nap. Shall I sing to you?

Roger Better not – she might hear you. We'll talk.

Sarah What shall we talk about?

Roger I'll tell you a story.

Sarah Oh yes.

Roger About our escape.

Sarah Oh yes.

Roger Well we can run away from this nasty house and our nasty Nanny, and we can escape and we'll – we'll – get on a spaceship –

Sarah A spaceship!

Roger	Yes – and we'll go sailing through space on this spaceship. There's everything you could possibly want in this spaceship, a jungle of trees to climb, a great huge sweetshop with as many sweets as we can eat.
Sarah	Oh yes – I can imagine the spaceship. It must be a huge ship sailing through the heavens, with great white sails. Is it like that?
Roger	Well... sort of.
Sarah	I wanted a ship like that for my birthday to sail on the pond in the park, but Nanny wouldn't let me have one as she said it wasn't suitable for a young lady. She said everyone in the park would laugh at me, but I don't think they would and anyway I think you should do what you like and not care about what people think, don't you?
Roger	I think you should go. I can hear Nanny coming back.
Nanny	Master Roger, I hope this day has taught you a lesson and that you have repented the evil that is in your heart. Now go back downstairs and get into bed without delay.
Roger	Psst! Sarah, she's gone. It'll be all right, Sarah. I'll think of something. There must be something we can do. And, thank you – you know – for today.

SCENE 8

Scene setter   The night passes and the next morning Roger is woken up by Elizabeth dragging the bedcovers off him.

Elizabeth   Wake up. Wake up, lazy bones!

Roger   Oh! It's you!

Elizabeth   Who did you think it was? Mum says you're to play with me.

Mum   Could you keep her occupied for a bit, Roger? I've got a bit of work to catch up with and there isn't any other time.

Roger   Why can't she play with her friends?

Elizabeth   They've all gone away for Christmas.

Roger   Oh.

Mum   Be an angel, Roger. I really must get on.

Roger   Oh, OK, but I want paying for it – for baby-sitting.

Elizabeth   Baby yourself.

Mum   Now just stop that. You might get to choose a video if you're good.

Elizabeth   That's not fair – *I* want to choose. He always chooses.

Roger	No I don't, you chose the last one!
Mum	Ooh, I give up! Just be good while I'm working.
Roger	What do you want to play then? Shall we play with the doll's house?
Elizabeth	I don't want to play with the silly old house. It's sissy. I want to play with my zoo. Yeah. ·I want to knock all the cages down and let the lions and tigers out – so they can eat people and gobble them all up and then be sick and chew the keeper's head off ... grrr ... grrr ... grrrr.

SCENE 9

Scene setter   They go off to play. That night when Roger comes back into the bedroom he is carrying a toy tiger.

Roger	I'll get her. I'll teach her, that horrible old Nanny. She's only an old doll after all, isn't she? I know how to get her. I'll put this tiger in her wardrobe. Then it can jump out and gobble her all up and she'll be dead, and Sarah won't have to suffer any more. That's what I'll do... There!
Scene setter	Roger puts the toy tiger in the attic wardrobe and walks away from the doll's house, but then he turns back again.
Roger	Or maybe it's not such a good idea! What if Sarah ...
Elizabeth	Roger! What are you doing?
Roger	Nothing.
Elizabeth	Keep away from my house.
Roger	Oh shut up. You never play with it.
Elizabeth	I don't care. You're not to touch it. Never ever ever. I'll scream.
Roger	Oh you're, you're – I hate you. I'm going to bed.
Scene setter	Elizabeth goes out and Roger creeps out of bed towards the doll's house to take the tiger out again. Before he can do so, Elizabeth comes in and sees him and lets out an ear-piercing scream.
Roger	Oh – oh – blow you! I really am going to bed!

Mum   Come on Elizabeth, bed now – Roger's been
in bed for ages and he's older than you.
(to herself) I'm going to take some of these
dolls for a spruce up. The nanny could do
with mending – her dress is a bit frayed, and
the mother and father and the cook –
they all need a stitch or two. I'll leave the boy
and girl till later. Night, darling! Night, Roger.

Scene setter   Roger is already asleep.

Scene 10

Scene setter Sometime later, Roger wakes up.

Roger I must take the tiger out! Before it's too late. Oh! It's too late – I'm back in the doll's house.

Scene setter Roger looks over at Sarah. She is fast asleep. He gets out of bed and goes over to the windows to look out.

Roger A street. Just an ordinary empty street. Street lamps and cobbles. I can't take Sarah out there in the middle of the night. What shall I do? There's a tiger upstairs and ...
by now surely there should be bangs and crashes and horrible groans. I know, I'll find Cook. I must tell someone.

Scene setter Roger goes downstairs to the kitchen. He enters very hesitantly, expecting to be grabbed.

Roger Cook? No one. There's no one here. I know, I'll go and find Sarah's parents.

Scene setter Back he goes upstairs.

Roger	Hallo! Hallo there! Excuse me – I ... No one – there's no one here but Sarah and me and the tiger. Maybe the tiger's eaten Nanny already and gone back to sleep! – Yes, that's why it's so quiet. And when it wakes up it'll be hungry again and it'll come to get its next meal and that'll be me and Sarah! Oh Sarah! I'm so, so sorry! I wish I could undo what I did! I wish I could go back to sleep right now and take the tiger out of the wardrobe. But I can't. I'm sorry! The tiger will eat you up and you'll never have a ship like the one you wanted to sail on the pond. Never climb trees. Oh Sarah!
Scene setter	Suddenly Roger grabs a large, heavy candlestick. He goes up the stairs to the attic. He listens at the door, then opens it very carefully, expecting to be pounced on. He hears purring and the wardrobe wobbles. He shuts the door carefully behind him.
Roger	It's stopped purring ... I can hear it growling! I'm going to open the door and let it out. I mustn't be scared, I must save Sarah!
Scene setter	Roger flings open the door and the tiger jumps out of the wardrobe and flies through the air. He crashes the candlestick down on the tiger's nose. The tiger stops and staggers and sinks slowly to the floor, unconscious.

Roger   I've saved Sarah! I've saved her!

Scene setter   Roger runs downstairs and into the bedroom. He jumps on his bed to tell Sarah but before he can say a word he faints!

Scene setter   When Roger wakes up he is back in his own room. He sees the doll's house, runs over to it and rescues the tiger.

Roger   You go back where you belong. With the other zoo animals!

Mum   Morning, you two. I've mended the dolls for the doll's house – they only needed a stitch or two. Now I can put them back.

Roger   Mum. Wait a minute – you know the Nanny doll...

Mum   This one?

Roger   Um – I don't want her to go back in the doll's house.

Mum   Why ever not? She's beautifully made – all those wooden joints. It's a real piece of Victorian craftsmanship.

Roger   I don't like her. She's got a horrible expression on her face and she's all strict and stiff. Please can we throw her away?

Mum   Oh we can't do that! She's an antique. We can't just throw her away. She belonged to your great granny. Besides, it's Elizabeth's house now.

Elizabeth   I don't like her either. She looks cross.

Mum   So she does! Do you know, I'd never noticed, but now you mention it ... I know – where are your paints? The paintbox you got last Christmas? Ah! Here it is.

Scene setter   Roger looks at Elizabeth. She is looking at him as if for the first time. Then she smiles at him. A really lovely smile.

Roger   What are you doing, Mum?

Mum   I'm painting a different face on the Nanny doll. ...There you are! A real transformation! Doesn't she look happy now!

Elizabeth   She's smiling!

Roger   Magic!

Elizabeth   I'm going to have my breakfast. Come on, Roger!

Roger   I won't be long, there's something I want to do first.

Scene setter   Several hours pass. Roger has been working hard, making something very small.

Dad   What are you doing, Roger?

Roger   There, I've made a ship, for the doll's house. It's a three-masted clipper and I've stitched all the sails. It's a present.

Dad	For the boy doll?
Roger	No, it's for the little girl, and her name is Sarah.
Dad	Hey you lot! Come and see what Roger's made to go in the doll's house.
Elizabeth	I want a ship! Just like that one! A bigger one, a real one! To sail on the pond in the park! Can I have one? Oh please can I have one?
Mum	Oh Elizabeth. You know ships like that cost the earth. And it isn't your birthday for ages!
Elizabeth	But I want one! I really want one!
Roger	I know! I'll make you a ship, a really good one, and I'll swap it with you for the doll's house. How about that? You'll help me, Mum, won't you?
Mum	I could do, I suppose. It'll be a lot of work for you though.
Dad	I wouldn't mind lending a hand. I know I'm not much good at that sort of thing but ... What do you say then, Elizabeth – is it a deal?
Elizabeth	OK, it's a deal. Great!
Roger	Thanks, Mum, for changing the Nanny doll. You know, it's funny, but I've got this kind of feeling that everything's going to be all right in the doll's house from now on.